What I like best

Yes, most of all

In my **Whole life**

Is . . .

PUFFIN BOOKS

First published in *Heard it in the Playground* 1989
Revised and abridged for this edition 2014
Dollywood edition published 2015

Printed in Spain 003

The authorized representative in the EEA is
Penguin Random House Ireland,
Morrison Chambers, 32 Nassau Street,
Dublin D02 YH68

A CIP catalogue record for this book is
available from the British Library

ISBN: 978–0–141–36118–5

MIX
Paper from responsible sources
FSC® C018179

Ball

NOT eating an ice-cream or riding a bike. NO – kicking a ball is what I like.

NOT reading a book or writing a letter.

NO – kicking a ball
is **TWENTY** times better!

My legs might be SKINNY

My feet might be SMALL

But I get a kick out of KICKING a ball.

Yes, kicking a ball

kicking a ball

With Clive and Trevor
Malcolm and Paul –
Or even without them
Just **ME**
and a . . .

...Wall.

Not PUNCHING a ball

Or BASHING a ball

SERVING a ball

Or SMASHING a ball

Not THROWING a ball

Or BLOWING a ball

Not BOWLING or BATTING

Or PATTING a ball

Not PINGING or PONGING

Or POTTING or PUTTING

BUT BOOTING and SHOOTING

SCRATCHHH!

Yes, kicking
oh, KICKING!
Just KICKING

a BALL.

A BALL in the playground ------------- A BALL on the grass -----

A BALL before breakfast ------------- A BALL before bed -------

--- A SHOT on the run ------------- A DRIBBLE, a PASS.

--- A dream of a BALL ----------- A 'GOAL' in the head.

Don't want a ball
That's **ODD** or *screw*
That you hit with a mallet
Or a billiard cue.

Don't want a ball
That's made of meat
I'd really rather
SCORE than eat!

NOT a ballcock
REFILL TUBE
FLOAT
TRIP LEVER
LIFT STRAP
TILT VALVE
PINION HOLDER
BALLCOCK
OR a ballpoint
Scapula
Humerus
OR a plastic ball-and-socket joint.
NOT a ball bearing
(bit too small)
BUT – putting it more or less
baldly –

A BALL.

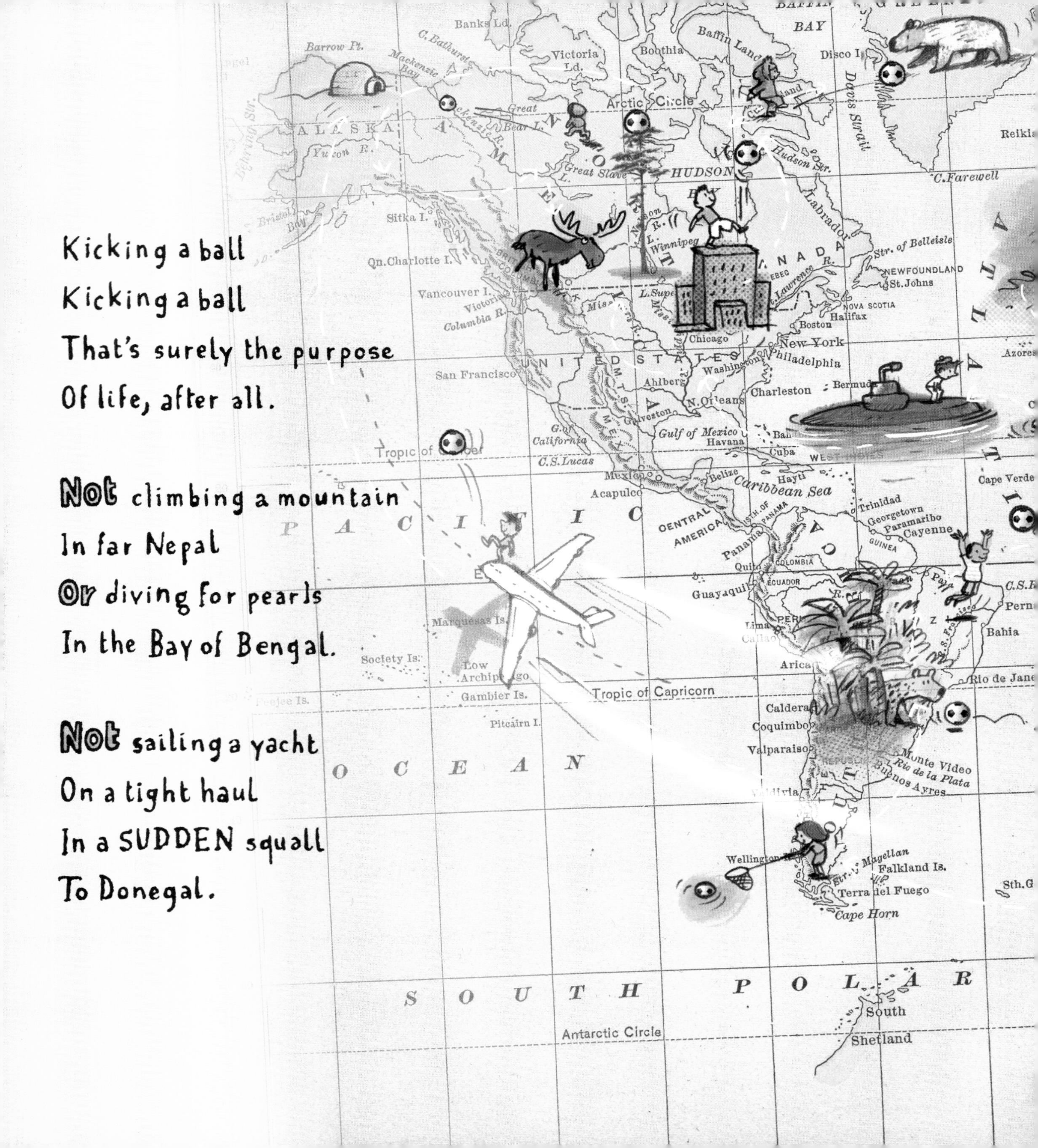

Kicking a ball
Kicking a ball
That's surely the purpose
Of life, after all.

Not climbing a mountain
In far Nepal
Or diving for pearls
In the Bay of Bengal.

Not sailing a yacht
On a tight haul
In a SUDDEN squall
To Donegal.

North C.
Hammerfest
Loffoden Is.
Arctic Circle
White Sea
Archangel
Yakutsk
Okhotsk
Bergen
Christiania
St. Petersburg
RUSSIA
Stockholm
Tobolsk
Sea of Okhotsk
KAMTCHATKA
Edinburgh
Liverpool
London
Hamburg
Amsterdam
Moscow
R. Irtish
L. Baikal
C. Lopatka
SAGHALIEN
Havre
Paris
GERMANY
AUSTRIA
Odessa
Volga
Astrakhan
Sea of Aral
L. Balkash
MONGOLIA
MAN-CHOORIA
Amoor R.
YEZO
Hakodadi
Danube
Black S.
CAUCASUS MTS.
Caspian Sea
TURKESTAN
CHINESE EMPIRE
Pekin
COREA
Sea of Japan
JAPAN
Tokio (Yedo)
Yokohama
ISLANDS
SPAIN
Constantinople
TURKEY
Bokhara
Astrabad
Mediterranean Sea
Beyrout
PERSIA
Cabool
Nagasaki
Shanghai
Nankin
MOROCCO
ALGIERS
TUNIS
TRIPOLI
Jerusalem
Bagdad
Persian G.
Cairo
EGYPT
Suez Canal
ARABIA
Delhi
INDIA
Canton
Amoy
Tropic of Cancer
Calcutta
Hong Kong
Red Sea
Mecca
Muscat
Bombay
Bay of Bengal
Bangkok
Mekong R.
China Sea
PHILIPPINE ISLANDS
Arabian Sea
Aden
C. Guardafui
Madras
Ceylon
C. Comorin
Malacca Str.
Singapore
Borneo
Caroline Is.
Molucca Is.
Equator
Gulf of Guinea
Sumatra
INDIAN
New Guinea
Solomon Is.
Flores Sea
Java
Torres Str.
Zanzibar
St. Paul de Loando
Benguela
Feejee Is.
St. Helena
Mozambique Chan.
Tananarivo
MADAGASCAR
Tropic of Capricorn
N.W. Cape
New Caledonia
Brisbane
OCEAN
Orange R.
Port Natal
CAPE COLONY
Cape Town
C. of Good Hope
Perth
C. Leeuwin
Great Australian Bight
Adelaide
Sydney
Melbourne
Bass Str.
Auckland
Tasmania
Hobart Town
Dunedin
PACIFIC OCEAN
ANTARCTIC OCEAN
Antarctic Circle
South Victoria
20
40
60
E WORLD

But kicking a ball

Kicking a ball

Kick,

kick,

kicking a BALL!

And later on
As the years pass
I'll still be running
Across the grass.

Kicking a ball
Kicking a ball
With Clive and Malcolm
Trevor and Paul.

Reading the paper, having a shave
Forcing the 'goalie' to make a save.

Kissing my wife, bathing our baby
Kicking a ball and SCORING (maybe).

Till baby toddles
And **tackles** and then ...

Starts the ball rolling
All over again.

What I like best, yes, most of all in my **whole life**, is kicking a ball.

In freezing cold ------------- or blinding heat ----------

Caked in mud ------------- covered in sweat -------

------------- EVER and ALWAYS, a ball at my feet.

------------- SCORING the GOALS I'll never forget.

Yes, life's a circle, endless and SMALL

And when all's said and done...

. . . the world's a BALL.